Watch

Beginners

An Informative Guide to Learning The
Basics Of Watch and Clock Repairing

J.B Lewis

Table of Content

Introduction

A watch is a little clock that people wear, enabling them to track time. It is also a fashionable accessory for men and women, and high-end watches are made for this purpose. It evolved from spring-powered clocks, which first appeared in the 14th century. Throughout most of its existence, it was a mechanical device powered by clockwork and kept time with an oscillating balance wheel. These are referred to as mechanical watches. Some watches have no battery, microchip, or circuitry, then what parts are machined to perfection, and what are the microscopic sizes and tolerances that can produce accuracy?

Learning how to repair and fix watches might seem hard, but with the basic information, you can acquire the skill. Watch maintenance is expensive, and those who can overhaul the mechanics, design the faces, and handle the repairs make good money. It may take time, but it will get you far. The maintenance and repair are taxing skills, but you will find it easier with a good selection of watch tools and information.

This book will give you just the knowledge you desire to know more about how the watch works, the different types of watches, and how to repair watches.

Chapter One

Portable spring-powered clocks were once considered a luxury that no aristocrat could afford. These portable timepieces, which were roughly the size of a desk clock and a pocket watch, could be attached to clothing or worn on a chain around the neck. With basic mechanical movements, the average clock had to be wound twice daily. Gentlemen would use these patterns, adorned with engravings and embellishments, as a symbol of elitism and riches. As the use of the timepiece became apparent, these clocks were largely employed by night watchmen to keep track of their shifts.

How the watch got its name

Many people think that the word "watch" first appeared in the vocabulary of night watchmen. An updated version of the Old English term "woecce," which directly translates to "watchman." Others maintained that the word was coined by sailors who used timepieces to keep track of their'shipboard watches,' which are today widely referred to as a shift or tour of duty.

Beginning in the early seventeenth century, watches began to appear on the cobblestone streets. Prior to the 1920s, practically all watches were mechanical pocket watches, also known as railroad or conductor watches due to their widespread usage by railroads.

However, when World Battle I broke out, American soldiers decided that reaching into a pocket to check the time while buried deep in the trenches of war was a preposterous notion, and thus the trench watch, now known as the 'wrist watch,' was born. It was invented by the Waltham Watch Company to allow soldiers to check the time while still looking down the sights of their guns.

Since then, watches have evolved drastically as new processes and intricacies were developed and watchmakers leapfrogged one after the other to outdo the competitors. Many consider watches to be an art form, and there are many different types and styles available today, ranging in price from a few dollars to millions of dollars for a one-of-a-kind grand complexity created in Switzerland by icons such as Patek Philippe, Vacheron Constantin, and so on.

Watch

Power is stored in the main spring and released in reliable increments by the escapement assembly. The gears connect the mainspring and escapement at various speeds, allowing the watch to tell time.

At a point in history, all watches were mechanical and required winding to be powered. Therefore, these watches were typically wound through the crown.

The crown tightens the mainspring inside the watch. The mainspring is the power source of all mechanical watches. Once wound, through a series of gears and components known as an escapement, the mainspring's tension is incrementally released, which powers the watch.

Automatic watches, also known as self-winding watches, have a weighted rotor mounted to the back of the movement. The rotor is usually shaped in a semicircle and is connected to the mainspring through a series of gears. With the motion of your wrist, the rotor spins on an axle. In doing so, it lines the mainspring and thus powers the watch.

A power reserve is the amount of time it takes for a fully wound watch to unwind. Most mechanical watches have a power reserve of between 36 and 42 hours. Therefore, the watch can run for that duration on a full line. However, some watches, like the IWC, also feature a complication called a power reserve indicator, which shows how much power remains in the watch. Refer to the manufacturer specs to familiarize yourself with what duration you can expect from your watch's power reserve.

Components of a Watch

1.   The crown: this is pulled out to set the time and pushed in to wind the watch. The setting jumper has indents to keep the crown mechanism locked in place.

Each mode gauges different gear sets. When the crown is pushed in for winding, the sliding pinion machines with gears are connected to the mainspring. When the crown is pulled outwards, the setting lever clicks into the second indent in the rigid setting jumper. At the same time, this setting level presses against the spring-loaded yoke. The yolk moves the sliding pinion into connection with the time-setting gears.

2.   Mainspring: the mainspring is a thin, nearly footlong strip of hardened metal coiled into a spring. It is contained by the mainspring barrel. It is connected to the winding pinion at one end and the mainspring barrel at the other.

The winding pinion moves independently of the barrel. A connected ratchet wheel and click assembly allow the pinion to rotate in only one direction. It prevents the spring from unwinding and ensures spring power can only exist through the barrier.

3.   The wheel train: the wheel train drives time keeping hands and associated wheels. The center wheel is driven by the mainspring barrel and rotates once per

hour. It holds the minute hand. Its 60 minutes journey is often divided into minute marks on the watch face.

The third wheel flows power through the fourth wheel. The first wheel rotates once per minute in incremental ticks. It also holds the second hand. Marks on the watch face can make it easier to see how many seconds have passed within a 1minute long revolution. The axle of each wheel rests in a synthetic jewel bearing. The near frictionless jewels can keep internal watch mechanics running smoothly for decades.

4.   The motion works: the motion works allow the watch to be freely rotated for time settings. It also performs a 12 to 1-speed reduction for the hour hand. Since the center wheel and minute hand rotate once per hour, the hour hand needs to make a much slower journey. It then completes a full rotation once every 12 hours as it passes by hour marks on the watch face.

The speed reduction is achieved as power flows from the cannon pinion through the minute wheel to the hour wheel. The cannon pinion and the wheel are press fit to the pinions that support them. It means that with enough force, they can be moved for time setting without disturbing the rigid underlying wheel train that drives them otherwise.

5.   The escapement and balance wheel: the balance wheel swings in a precise rhythm, knocking the pallet fork back and forth, allowing the escape wheel to move and releasing mainspring power in small increments.

6.   The balance wheel: the balance wheel is the most fragile part of the watch. It is supported by a shock absorbers mounting system with a jewel bearing and capstone. It protects sensitive parts from impact. For example, if the watch is dropped, the hairspring partly drives the balance.

7.   The escapement: the pallet fork and the escape wheel from the escapement is a clever exchange of power that forms the heart of mechanical watch operation. Driven by the hairspring, the balance wheel impulse pumps into one side of the pallet fork. It

releases the opposing pallet jewel from its locked position against an escape wheel tooth. Just as the pallet jewel slips free, the specially shaped escape wheel tooth delivers a little impulse of power from the mainspring through the pallet fork. This, in turn, pushes the impulse pin launching the balance wheel into another swing. The process repeats as long as the watch has mainspring power.

The hairspring has regulator pins to adjust the active length of the spring. It alters the balance wheel swing rate and, as such, the speed of the entire watch. This means regulating a watch that keeps time too fast or too slow. A pallet jewel makes the characteristic watch ticking sound as they catch escape wheel teeth. Each incremental escape wheel rotation is called a beat. The common watch beat rate is 21,600 beats per hour, equal to 6 beats per second.

8.   Supporting structure: various specially shaped metal plates support watch internals. The main plate serves as the base.

The barrel bridge holds the mainspring barrel and associated parts.

The train wheel bridge supports the wheel train.

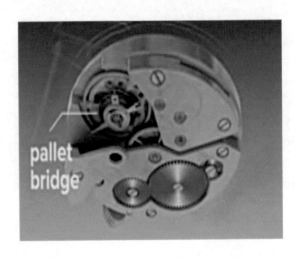

The pallet bridge holds the pallet fork.

The balance bridge supports the balance wheel and regulator assembly.

9. The bridge is a piece of metal, often brass, that the gears sit in. It is essentially the chassis of a watch. The average watch movement will have around 5 bridges.

10. Jewel: jewels refer to tiny pieces of synthetic sapphire and ruby that serve to make watches more accurate. Jewels can be found in a few places in a mechanical watch. Jewel bearings are at the center of most gears creating the lowest possible amount of friction. These can often be seen on a movement as tiny ruby-colored circles. They can also be found on the tips of a pallet fork and the impulse pin. They reduce wear

on the movement and lower friction to improve efficiency.

11.   The oscillating weight is the mechanism that automatically winds the main spring in an automatic movement. It is a half circle that uses the wearer's motion, combined with gravity, to wind the watch.

How a Mechanical Clock Works

A mechanical watch is any watch that is powered by a mechanism to measure time instead of quartz. A mechanism is often referred to as a movement or caliber. A quartz watch uses a small piece of quartz crystal with an electronic signal that pulses through it, creating a consistent vibration for the quartz to measure time. Quartz watches are extremely accurate because of the high frequency at which quartz vibrates.

Types of mechanical movements:

1.   Manual movement

2.   Automatic movement

The manual watch movement must be regularly wound to keep the watch running, while automatic movements, once fully wound, can maintain their time keeping if worn regularly. This is because a mechanical watch will have a power reserve. The power reserve measures how long the watch will run before it stops. An average mechanical watch has a power reserve of around 48 hours. The power reserve is constantly running out on a manual watch, so you need to wind the watch regularly. An automatic watch can maintain its power reserve because of the movement's design.

The official Swiss chronometer testing institute

This independent organization tests the isochronism of a watch movement. Isochronism is the same principle that allows a pendulum swing to be equal on both sides. A manufacturer like Rolex will send just the movement to the organization, and they will perform a series of tests to determine if the movement is within the standards. The most recognized criteria for the certification is the average daily rate of -4,+6 or up to 10 seconds per day. If the movement meets the standard as well as the others, the movement receives the chronometer certification.

The movement is then returned to the manufacturer and assembled into a watch. The organization does not guarantee movement abilities after the test. Rather than at the point when it was tested, it could maintain the standards. A watch with the chronometer certification will not always operate within these standards. The certification means that a movement met the criteria at one point.

Difference between Quartz, Mechanical and automatic watches.

Watches come with 3 different types of movements:

1.   Battery-powered quartz. Seiko introduced quartz in 1959. They were so cheap, accurate and easy to mass produce, and they are almost more accurate than mechanical or automatic watches.

2.   Mechanical watches are hand-wound timepieces that use hundreds or even thousands of tiny little

mechanical parts to keep the watch running as long as it is wound. Many hand-wound watches can be sold at higher prices. The main advantage of the mechanical watch over a quartz watch is that a mechanical watch will last for a very long time when kept wound. A Quartz watch will last for a long time but will inevitably die. If a mechanical watch is built well and taken care of, it could last for generations. The mechanical movements are like the top echelon.

3.   An automatic watch will keep ticking even if you do not manually wind it. As long as you wear it on your wrist, the motion of your arm keeps the watch wounded. It does this using an off-center weighted rotor that spins as you move throughout the day. As it turns, it activates a ratchet system which keeps the watch wound. Though, automatic watches are not more accurate than mechanical watches. The advantage is that they keep ticking even if you do not wind them.

Automatics have a power reserve. It means it will keep ticking when fully wounded for a long time. If you see an automatic watch that says it has a 48hour power reserve, it will be ticking 48hours when fully wound.

The length of the power reserve varies between different models and different brands. It is safe to assume that most automatic watches will keep ticking for 48 hours. You would have to reset it whenever it stops ticking. If it has a date window, wind it if it has a hand winding movement or shakes it to get it going. It starts winding itself back up with the movement of your arm. If you do not like having to wind and reset your watches, you can put your automatic watch in a watch winder.

The watch winder is like a little storage device that turns the watch slowly to keep the movement rotating even when you are not wearing it. Automatic watches can be very expensive depending on the craftsmanship, where it was made and how many complications it has. Complications include a date window, power reserve meter or anything beyond the basic hour, minute and second hand.

Watch companies that make their movements and house their watches will be very expensive. If you are wondering why the prices vary so much for watches that use the exact movement, it is because you are paying for a brand's name or luxury item.

Chapter Two

Ten Things That Could Damage Your Watch

1.   Dropping the watch: the shock depends on what you drop it on. The best way to avoid this is to get a G shock watch. If you will be doing something that is potentially going to damage the watch, the best thing is to take it off or have a beta watch specifically for that role. For example, you do not want to mow the lawn or do some other things wearing your dress watch. In storing them, please do not keep them on the ledge of the shelf. Keep them away from the reach of children.

2.   Forcibly winding the watch: This applies to manual watches. Do not put too much force while whining. It will break the crown. Be conscious of what you are doing. As you get to the top, start noticing a little resistance. Treat it slowly and gently.

3. Setting functions wrong: this applies mostly to set the date function. All watch movements vary. They all do have a danger zone. Cycle through the date change takes 11:00 to 3:00 in the morning. Try to avoid setting the date at that time. Always refer to your watch instruction manual for safe date-changing procedures. It can also apply to several complications.

4. Improper watch storage: this mainly has to do with temperature and moisture. Stop storing your watches anywhere that is damp or moist. You can also use a moisture-absorbing agent with new bags, shoes or clothes. Put it into your watch box or case to remove any additional moisture. Avoid high or low temperatures, especially high temperatures. High temp can muck up the oils that lubricate the movements in the watch. It could lead to friction in the mechanical parts and damage the watch. You want to keep your watch in a room with a steady room temperature.

5. Exposing it to a magnetic field: this is a silent killer for your wristwatch. You can easily tell that your watch is magnetized because it will start running fast

suddenly. Avoid things that give out magnetic fields like speakers, speakers in your laptop, or phones. If phones vibrate, a little motor makes them vibrate and can magnetize your watch. Having a quartz watch or mechanical watch can be a good deterrent.

6.   Using your chronograph underwater: by pressing the pushes underwater, this compromise can allow water to get into the watch. The solution to this is to use the dive time bezel. If you have screw-down pushes on the watch, ensure they are screwed down before you get in the water.

7.   Mucking up the threading or damaging the crown while winding or setting the time: it is very easy and convenient to set the time or screw the crown on the wrist, but it is best to take it off first. Unknowingly, you are doing it at an angle and do not want to muck up the threading, especially if it is a screw-down crown. Make sure it is always screwed down; if it is not a screw-down crown, ensure it is in its proper position. Always take your watch off when you are setting or screwing the

crown or anything like that. Do not also screw it in too tightly. You might muck up the seal or gasket. However, it does not have to be too tight. The crown is usually the most vulnerable part.

8.   Taking care of your watch: a sign that your watch needs a service is when it is starting to run slow or lose time. Make sure that you keep your watch serviced. The worst thing you can do is have a watch for about seven years without servicing it. After that, it can damage the watch permanently. Also, if you are storing a watch in a safe place, you can take it out every few weeks to wind it to give it a full charge. Finally, make sure the oils and everything in there are running.

9.   Wearing the watch in the shower or long baths: remember that saltwater will corrode the seals and gaskets over time. If you go beach or fishing wearing your watch, ensure that the seals and gaskets are replaced. You can also avoid taking the watch into the water. The beta watch is a great way to get around this

too. Be wary of how regularly you expose your watch to water.

10.   Do-it-yourself repairs: wristwatch making is a real talent and requires a very steady hand in the real profession. Even with the most basic movements, you need to do, take it to a professional. The art of watchmaking takes years.

Things to note before buying a mechanical watch

1.   Mechanical watches require maintenance, and maintenance does cost money. However, mechanical watches will last for a while, probably 5 to 10 years.

They require some servicing because of the internals of a mechanical watch. There are gears, springs and things that wear down. There are lubricants and oil that need to be replaced. If you ignore these, the watch will not function well and eventually stop working. The maintenance of a mechanical watch can cost more than the watch itself.

2. Mechanical watches are not very accurate compared to your cell phone's time. But, on the other hand, your cell phone connects to a server and gets the exact atomic time with incredible accuracy.

A typical mechanical watch is going to lose around 20 seconds. So you might have to reset it from time to time to keep it up to date.

3. Mechanical watches do not need batteries, but they need to be powered by something. It is powered by a spring that is wound up tightly. The spring can be wound in several ways. It can be a hand wound or winding through the crown.

It could also be an automatic movement through the movement of your wrist. Mechanical watches last for about 40 hours after fully wound. They would stop working after 40hours. You would have to wind and reset it to work again.

4. The actual ownership of a mechanical watch means you will frequently reset the time and date. If

you are wearing and keeping it wound all the time, you will be resetting it to get it back at the right time.

5.   Even though you are resetting the time lot, not all mechanical watches have certain features that make that easier. Two of the common features you find on mechanical watches are called hacking and hand whining. Hacking means that the second-hand will stop when you pull the crown out. It allows you to set the watch very accurately to the second. Push the crown back, and it will be set to that time. The hand winding feature is taking the crown and spinning it. It will make it wind.

Chapter Three

Useful Tools for Watches and Clocks

Straps and bracelets

One of the easiest ways to get excited about your watch is to change the strap and bracelet or get it sized up perfectly. To do this, you must have some basic tools to make it happen.

Spring bar tool: You can get these for between five to ten dollars on places like amazon. Depending on your needs, you can also get additional ends: straight ends and fork end. Straight ends will be great for drilled lugs and changing out straps. The fork swaps a strap when trying to get hold of a spring on the back of the case.

Pin block: you would need a bracelet pin block. It is used to hold a bracelet in place vertically to remove pins. It can also hold a bracelet while you are unscrewing and screwing. They are cheap. They add stability and a steady hand to doing this process.

Spring bar pliers: This tool allows you to hold a bracelet and smoothly push out a pin simultaneously. It does this by squeezing like you would with a set of pliers. There is a back for pushing pins back in too. They make work so much easier than normal.

Spring bar tweezers are useful when dealing with certain types of watches with openings on both sides to grab the spring. It gives you more control over taking out a spring without worrying about scratching up the back of the log.

Storage

Watch roll: If traveling, the cheapest and most great way to bring three to four watches with you is to use a watch roll. It folds up so that the watches do not touch each other. They can be leather, canvas etc. You can also make use of a watch pouch. It is a nice way to bring one additional watch without worrying about damage. It is one of the best ways to ensure that the watch will not get scratched. The pouches also have a space to insert the watch so that it does not scratch the case back.

A standard display box is a great way to organize, display and keep watches safe.

Winders: Using winders is a nice way to keep your watch running. There are attainable ones and expensive ones. Winders that are motor powered are going to be a bit more expensive.

Maintenance

Polish: It is used to maintain acrylic crystal watches prone to scratch. It is a paste that you can apply to the face of a watch. It will help with the micro-abrasions and scuffs on acrylic crystals to be polished off. Make sure there is no surface-level treatment or coating on the crystal. It could create a worse result. It is really useful when dealing with vintage watches, watches that have acrylic crystal and are prone to scratch.

Another form of polishing is going to be with cases. Again, a Cape Cod cloth is recommended. It is cool for small marks on bracelets or the side of a case. Also, it will help with some basic scratches on your watch case.

Caseback tools:

• A watch back removal tool would help to screw open case backs. It has an adjustable prong to grab different size case-backs.

• A case back friction ball will help to open the watch if that is not tightly sealed. Add friction and twist. The case back will come off.

• A case back knife will be for snap-on case backs and not screwed-on case backs. It is for the little part on the side of a case, and you could place a tape on it to grab it.

Set of screwdriver: This is specifically made for watch screws. When dealing with adjusting expensive bracelets, you do not want the screws to get completely mauled and do not have access to sizing your bracelet again. So be careful to get the right screwdriver to ensure that you will not do any permanent damage. The basic watch toolkit contains the basic things you need for your wristwatch.

Digital calipers: It is used for reviewing watches. It is also used to measure the size of a watch. These are also useful if you have a collection of vintage pieces. When buying watches online, look at your collection and know all the dimensions of the watches that you currently own and what your preferred sizes are. It is going to help you get informed as a buyer.

Time-graphers: Time-graphers are great if you are curious as a watch collector or regulator. The time graph gives you a few things. First, it is going to give your beat frequency and accuracy rating.

Loops: These are great because they help you see details on a watch. It also gives the idea of ensuring the watch is in good condition.

Demagnetizer or degausser: Magnetic fields are not your friend when it comes to the oscillation of the balance wheel on a watch, specifically the hairspring. Unless the hairspring does not have some magnetic components and materials, once the coils of a hairspring are magnetized, a hairspring can be attracted to each other during the oscillation. And even stick together. It is not so good as it effectively shortens the hairsprings and causes the watch to gain or lose time or stop working. The good thing about getting a demagnetizer or degausser is that you turn on the machine, pass a watch through the opening a few times, do a quick check on your time-grapher then you are good to go.

Things to note about a watch

To most people living around technology, getting hold of inaccurate data is as hard as lifting a phone or a tablet. That kind of complacency does not just affect the most tech-savvy. For most people who still enjoy the beat of a balanced wheel, a self-changing date is a modern convenience. Mechanical watches have only been imbued with a self-changing date since the 1940s and a quick change date for even less time than that.

The self-changing date takes over at around midnight, advancing the date forward by one day, assuming the next day is not the first. Five times a year, plus the time you leave your watch run down, the date falls out of sync. The date window will then need to be adjusted. The quick set date function was created to address the minor inconvenience. This feature offers the ability to easily slip through the dates to select the number you choose with utmost expediency. Most date changes do not happen instantly. Some even snap from one number to the next at 12:00. Being a mechanism of slow-moving gears and wheels, most take about four hours to transition fully. While the date wheel is engaged with the mechanism and changing, an adjustment with the quick set feature could damage the driving teeth and even shear them off completely. For most watches, it is advised to avoid using the quick set date between 10:00 pm and 2:00 am. Your watch's manual will confirm. If you are unsure whether your watch is showing morning or evening, advance the hands until the date changes. It will be calibrated to midnight.

Like the precursor of digital music, the cassette tape, these tickets use magnetism in the strip to store information about whatever it is you are trying to access and whether or not it will let you in. Tiny speakers in your phone contain magnets and are responsible for stripping your ticket of data and the subsequent altercation with a ticket inspector. These little speakers are everywhere with their little magnets and are bad news for your watch.

More and more watches are being manufactured with anti-magnetically materials. However, there are far more watches that have no resistance to magnetism. A watch relies on such a delicate balay of motion to run, so something as invasive as magnetism can cause utter chaos. The effect occurs primarily with the hairspring - the fine coil of wire takes how far the balance wheel can bounce in and out.

The regulation determines the speed at which the watch runs. It doesn't take much time to alter its behavior. When it becomes magnetized, it binds together and cannot separate the turns. It effectively shortens the spring and makes the beat faster, speeding the threat up considerably. You can get your watch demagnetized at your nearest retailer, which will return to normal.

Unless you are an active diver or an astronaut, you must never wear your watch over the top of your clothing. Watchmakers have been devising ways to make their watches more impervious to foreign objects. Unfortunately, dust and moisture in a movement are a recipe for disaster, slowing it down and rusting it solid. Wearing it on a sleeve or in a pocket is no great challenge for day-to-day use. A simple covering is enough to keep a movement lint-free and serviceable for many years. However, the advent of underway exploration is not good enough.

Water has the habit of being able to make its way into almost anything. Watchmakers task themselves with overcoming this challenge, refining designs from clunky housings that fully encompass the watch to the watch itself becoming waterproof housing. It was achieved with compression seals bound tight with precise screw threads. You must unscrew the crown on your dive watch before setting the time. The matter is not so clear with the chronograph. Unscrewing the crown underwater would cause disaster for your watch, but the same is not quite so widely understood of chronograph pushers. On some divers, the pushers have an outer sleeve that requires unscrewing before use. That is not to seal the pusher but rather to lock it.

Chapter Four

How to Resize Your Metallic Watch Band

• Get your push pin to push the little pins on the watch band through.

• Get your needle nose pliers to help pull things through.

• Get a small hammer and a supporting structure to set the watch band.

• Place your band where you can hit down, and there will be a little spot or hole for the pin to come out.

• Set the push pin on it and hit it with a hammer for the band's pin to come out on the other side. It will protrude a little bit from the band.

• Use the needle nose pliers to pull it out. The band will be disconnected.

• Remove the next pin on the band with the same method used in pulling out the first pin. That part of the band will be removed.

- Now, you can rejoin. Keeping in mind that the split part of the pin will go in first.

- Use your hammer to tap it back all the way in.

How to Fit A New Glass Watch

There are several types of glasses for watches;

a.   Mineral glasses

b.   Sapphire glasses

c.   Perspex glasses

d.   Flat glasses

e.   Domed glasses

f.   Armoured glasses

g.   Shaped glasses and so on.

An armoured glass is a perspex with a tension ring around its inner part. The tension ring is black. You also can get steel and gold colour.

- Open the watch

- Remove the movement so that you can remove the old glass.

You can now remove the glass with the movement from the watch case. They are quite a tight fit. You might not be able to push them out with your fingers. Instead, use a glass press to make it easier for yourself. You can use any form of glass press made by version or horotec, and there are some good budget glass presses you can get off eBay. Use the glass press to push out the glass watch. In case your glass press is using aluminium dyes, use a bit of plastic over it to protect the watch case from getting scratched. Some presses have nylon dyes which help to prevent scratches.

- Place the glass loosely into the bezel of the watch.

- Set it up in the machine again using a bit of plastic to prevent scratches on the new glass.

- Add a beat of tension, not too much to crack the glass. It will seal itself. You will feel almost like a click as it goes in.

An armoured glass is water resistant, so the pressure exerted against the case due to the tension ring will usually create a watertight seal. Reassemble the watch, and you will be good to go.

Ten Watches to Avoid Buying

Replica or fake watches: Do not buy these types of watches because they infringe on trademarks. It means taking an authentic watch and its design and brand and then blatantly using its brand, logo, trade mark and claiming it as your own. This is, of course, illegal. Manufacturing these watches is illegal. Selling, transporting and distributing these watches are illegal. Counterfeit goods are illegal in the United States. Other parts of the world may be a little bit lenient. You could face jail time and litigation. It is not good to copy someone's work, claiming it as your own and taking their trademark and identity. Also, you would not want to look down and lie to yourself every time you wear your watch. You do not need to buy fake watches. You would not feel good being able to put something like that on the wrist. You can get a real watch in its own identity for the same amount of money you might buy the fakes for. Having a genuine wristwatch will give you more peace of mind.

Homage watch: There are two different types of this watch. Some will still have their own identity or do it differently, and some will be a direct copy. Get a watch with its own design identity that is not copied from anywhere else. Taking shared ideas and building upon them is okay, but not entirely copying them.

Unproven upstart brand: These are upstart watches with no watchmaking track record. They have no interest in trying to make a good product. They are just trying to make a quick buck. You could see them on Instagram with aggressive advertisements. If you cannot find any track records of individuals that own it or have reviews, or there is no one talking about it, it could be a random copy brand. If any of these come in front of you and you cannot identify reviews or someone who has an experience with that brand anywhere on the internet, it is a good sign that it is probably an unproven brand.

Watches that cause financial hardship: Avoid watches that put a little more stress on yourself than you should. Do not put a burden on yourself when buying a watch. You should be able to afford, buy, and not feel it. There might be more serious things in your life that you have to prioritize before you start spending money on watches. Do not be the type of person that owns a watch and does not have a bed frame for your bed. Be responsible and thoughtful.

Fashion department store watches: High-end fashion brands have watches that are not made to create the best quality product and any thoughtfulness involved in watchmaking. They are watches that are in department stores that come with markups.

Watch Rules

• On what wrist should you wear your watch? It depends on the wrist that suits you. Wear your watches on your non-dominant hand wrist. In other words, if you are right-handed, you should wear your watch in your left hand. On the other hand, you should wear your watch in your right hand if you are left-handed. This is mainly to make your watches obtrusive while doing your simple daily task.

Wear watches on the non-dominant side because we are more active with our dominant hand. We carry things with the dominant hand. It's stronger and steadier and so on. You do not want to risk damaging the watch while doing all of those with your dominant hand. So choose the wrist that is most comfortable for you.

- Wear a watch for the right occasion. Think of watches like shoes. There is not one style that fits all scenarios. Just like you would not wear sneakers to go to a funeral, you cannot wear a cheap G-Shock watch with an extensive custom suit or an expensive luxury watch with basketball shorts and a T-shirt. A watch should enhance your outfit. It is an accessory and should not create a distraction.

- Your wristwatch should go before your wristband. It should not be on it or after it. This is so that you would get a full range of motion on your wrist. When you wear a watch, you do not want it to be obtrusive. It will be painful by the end of the day because you will be reducing the natural mobility of your wrist. Anytime your wrist goes back even slightly, it will cause pain.

- Your watch needs to fit right. If you want the watch to sit before your wrist bone, the watch needs to be fitted for your wrist. Please do not wear a loose watch that looks like it is about to fall out. It is going to make you look like a noob. Leather band watches allow you to adjust the watch to your wrist, so it fits properly. If you have a metal link bracelet, you will want to visit some jewellery shops where they would properly size it for your wrist.

When it comes to sizing, you do not want it to be so tight that it cuts your circulation to keep the watch in place. You also do not want it to be loose where it is moving around all the time. Your comfort level should be able to fit at least one finger. Your index finger should be able to fit in between your watch and your wrist. It should give you enough comfort throughout the day.

- The size of your watch: Just like you would want your clothing to fit you, your watch should also fit you right to suit your body shape. Your wristwatch should be anywhere from 35 to 42 millimetres for men. Anything smaller would be in the woman's territory. Do not wear a watch with a face that is way too big. There is no specific size to be considered too big for a watch. It depends on the size of your wrist. The oversized wristwatches are clunky and heavy, drawing too much attention. Your watch is just an addition to your outfit.

- Find the right strap for your watch: Many people prefer going with stainless steel for an everyday watch. Some like the rubberized strap or leather strap. It all depends on what is comfortable for you. It also depends on your style. The rubber strap will not work if you wear a more formal outfit. The leather strap is better than it.

- On the other hand, the stainless steel or rubber would fit well if you are into casual clothing. Think about your everyday style, personal style and wear and when you will wear this watch to get the right strap. Then, buy a strap that will be easy to mix and match with most of your favourite outfits.

- Be careful with SmartWatches: Smartwatches are not very elegant. So be mindful of the outfit that you are wearing with it. If you are all suited up and looking amazing, a smartwatch could completely ruin that look.

Chapter Five

Cleaning A Watch Movement

Watch cleaning machines are quite expensive and are not made anymore. Their new machines are extremely expensive and cost several thousands of pounds. However, it will be utmostly useful and will last you. They use little baskets to hold all the watch parts in several different sections.

- The watch's movement is placed into the basket and the cleaner.

- It spins around in the cleaning solution.

- It is then placed in a rinse solution and another rinse solution.

- It goes into the heating element of the cleaner, where it will dry off and is ready to be checked and assembled. What was initially probably grubby and dirty will come out nice and clean. These machines are the best way of cleaning a watch's movement.

Not everyone is going to have access to acquire these rather expensive machines. Not using a movement cleaner machine takes a slightly longer process and manual labour. The best alternative is to get yourself an ultrasonic cleaning machine. Do not go for the cheapest on eBay because they are not that good and powerful. They won't last long enough. Instead, invest in something of good quality.

Cleaning with an ultrasonic cleaner: Many people mistake stripping the watch down into parts and putting all those parts directly into an ultrasonic cleaning machine. Instead, you will need something like a Kilner jar. It is also called a jam jar.

- Fill the jar with a cleaning fluid and place the jar into the ultrasonic cleaning machine. The ultrasonic cleaning machine will have some warm water in it.

- Place the movement into the jar.

- Dry them off on a paper towel.

- Get your rinse jar.

-       Place the movement into the rinse solution and do the same in the ultrasonic cleaner.

-       Take the rise solution out.

-       Put the parts on a paper towel and allow them to dry in the air.

In terms of the fluids you can use inside the jar, it will vary depending on where you are. They are professional chemicals and should be treated with caution and great care. You can use normal jewellery cleaning fluid if you do not want to go out with expensive cleaners. It will be better to mix them with demineralized water. You do not need a huge amount. For the rinse solution, you can use lighter fuel that would evaporate, like alcohol, Zippo fuel or petrol lighter fuel, maybe. They will do just enough job as well.

Basically:

•   Get yourself an ultrasonic cleaning machine

•   Fill it with warm water.

•   Get a couple of jars, one with a cleaning solution and the other with a rinse solution.

- Get mini baskets like amazon or eBay to fill the basket with various watch parts. Then, the larger parts can go into the fluid directly. In that way, you won't get all the parts mixed up.

- Place it inside your cleaning solution.

- Put the cleaning solution inside the ultrasonic cleaner for 20 minutes.

- Take it out

- Put the baskets in a second with a rinse solution for about 20 minutes.

- Lay it down on a tissue to let it dry.

- Have your third jar with another rinse solution. Put them into that and place them into the ultrasonic cleaner.

- Take them out and allow them to dry in the air. In that way, you will get a nice and clean watch movement.

Outside of professional cleaning, the ultrasonic cleaner is the only option. If you have a bit of money and patience, you can only go to places like eBay to get used machines that will cost a fraction of the price of a new one. You could also get a Brenray watch and a clock cleaning machine. They are easy to refurbish as well. You can also come to watch cleaning machines that can spin and have an ultrasonic component.

How to dismantle a mechanical watch

Using an AS 1900 movement watch

- Start by removing the hands of the watch.

- The dial is secured to the movements. Two dial screws must be loosened and not unscrewed until they fall out. Then, loosen them enough for the dial to come off.

- Once the dial is removed, you can retighten the screws.

- Gently pry the dial away from the movement very carefully. Be careful not to bend the dial fate as it would cause alignment issues when trying to refit it.

- Remove the calendar plates.

- With the dismantling of watches, always release tension from springs before unscrewing them.

- Remove the calendar cover plates, secured by two screws. Be careful when lifting them, as the spring will potentially fly across. Use peck wood to hold the spring down as you slowly pry up the cover plate.

- Release the tension on your spring. Use your tweezers to take the spring away.

When dismantling a watch, the general idea is to start with removing the calendar works first.

Next is the motion work, which is the hour wheel and minute wheel. On the AS 1900, a spring also holds the minute wheel unusually under tension. Make sure that when you put it back together, you put the wheel down on the right side of the spring.

- Release any winds from the mainspring. To do that, put a little bit of pressure on the whiner.

- Move the clicks forward and then hold it when it is at its furthest point. Use your tweezers to push it even further. Let go of the winder gently to prevent breakage of the main spring.

- Continue dismantling the watch, unscrew and remove the balance. Carefully lift the balance upwards. Lift it safely with tweezers and place it on the workbench.

- Remove the pallet cock. Be very careful when removing the pallet cock.

- Remove the wheel and the crown wheel. Next, unscrew the ratchet wheel screw to remove the ratchet wheel.

- The crowns are secured with a left-handed screw. There is a little shim present. Remember not to lose that shim.

- Moving the clicks and the click spring. Use your peg wood to prevent the click spring from flying off.

- The barrel bridge is secured with two screws. Undo the screw so that you can remove the bell bridge.

- Gently remove the balance wheel and the barrel.

- Use a screwdriver to lift the bridge gently. The train wheels will now be exposed.

- Gently use your tweezers to remove the four wheels together with the escape wheel.

- Flip the movement over to remove the rest of the components under the dial.

- Remove the labour spring secured with just one screw. That whole section is called the keyless work.

- Remove the setting wheel and the settings lever, secured with a setting lever screw.

- Remove the crown and winding stem. It allows the removal of the clutch wheel and winding pinion.

- Remove the mainspring from the barrel using a staking block and a pair of brass tweezers. They will make the mainspring guaranteed clean. If you use your hands to remove the mainspring, ensure you have a tight grip on both the spring and the barrel. If you do not remove the mainspring, you will know if it is not broken. You must replace the mainspring if it is broken or has hairline fractures.

- Place all the dismantled parts in a basket for cleaning.

How to Remove and Replace Watch Movements

There are various reasons to remove or replace a watch movement, such as; straightening the hands, cleaning it out or replacing a broken movement or crystal. The first step is to:

1.   Determine the watch back type. Then, gather the necessary tools to remove it.

2.   Remove the back of the watch. Be careful not to let any dirt or dust particulate fall into the opened watch. It can cause damage to the movement. Set the watch back aside in your parts tray.

3.   Determine the type of release mechanism on your model of watch. Once you know the release type, you can remove the watch stem. The watch stem changes the hands and is sometimes used to wind a watch. It is attached to the crown and is connected to the movement with a release mechanism.

4.   There are a few ways to remove the watch stem. The most common is the list release style. Before setting your watch onto your work surface, place a soft cloth or clean pad to ensure it does not scratch your crystal.

Grasp the crown while pushing down on the simple with the tweezers. The location of the release varies from watch to watch. It is usually close to where the stem is attached to the movement and may have an arrow pointing. Press down on the button to release the stem. Grab the edge of the crown and pull it away from the movement. You may need to use your fingernail to get under the crown. Pull the stem out of the watch and set the stem aside in your parts tray.

5.   There will be a plastic movement ring holding the watch movement in place. In some cases, this will come out with the movement, and some may not. Pull on this until it comes out of the watch case. Set the watch movement and movement ring aside carefully. To put your move back into the watch, ensure all the dirt and particles are removed from the watch case.

Have the stem position of the face pointing towards the hole in the watch case, faced down. Set the plastic ring onto the movement if it becomes separated. Take the stem from your parts tray and slide it through the hole in the watch case and into the corresponding hole in the movement. Push it in gently while turning until you hear a click. If it does not go in easily, do not force it. Make sure everything is aligned correctly. When the stem is attached to the watch movement and turns accordingly, you can attach your watch back.

Chapter Six

Watch lubrication

First, use a fluorescent type of lubrication. It helps with quality control to see that the lubrication is correctly applied and isn't moving into parts where you do not want it to go.

• The first lubricant you would get would be a form of grease - Mobius 8300 and 8301 grease. 8301 is a very good natural grease. It is very good for lots of applications.

• Microglist-d series lubricant. Micro clips d5 is a medium viscosity oil. It is reasonably thick. It is a very good general-purpose oil for lots of things. For example, it can go on clocks and watch movements.

• Sinterlube 9010. It is a fluorescent lubricant. The standard 9010 is pale blue. It comes in two millimetres which is the smallest amount you can buy. However, two millimetres is enough to service many watches.

These three lubricants come with three different reasons and categories.

-	You have the grease, which is fairly thick. Then we have the medium oil and the 9010, a very fine oil. The 9010 is a fine oil. It is good for fast-moving parts such as balance capsules, pallet stones, train wheel gears, escape wheels and pallet stuff.

-	The Microglist d5 or any of the d series would be good for slower-moving things with slightly higher torque. Things like centre wheel arbours and the application of canon pinions, the outer barrel arbour walls, crown wheels and so on.

-	The natural grease 83 series can be used for lots of things;

-	It can be used for the inside of a barrel arbour

-	It can be used for the mainspring setting, lever spring setting, spring clutch, wheel winding pinion, etc. It works for anything that is very slow-moving and requires grease.

- It is not good for things that turn, such as wheels or train wheels, but it is good for metals.

Tips for Lubricating Watches

• It is important to lubricate the watch after it comes out of the cleaner. If the movement parts, bridges, jewels and so on are dirty or not clean during the oiling process, you are doing shoddy work. It is bad workmanship to the oil without proper cleaning first. Dust, dirt and debris from the movement may still be present, creating a grinding paste. Also, lubricating the oil incorrectly will cause the oil to spread and deteriorate earlier rather than later. Any oil application on an already dirty movement will only have a temporary effect and, in the long run, make matters worse.

• Independent watchmakers make one of the most common mistakes: Not using quality oils. Instead, they buy cheaper generic oil versions or start experimenting with other oils from different industries. Although, it is not bad to experiment. Make sure to buy the right oil for the job. If the technical guide tells you to use a particular oil, then use it. Do not use motor oil from your 92Honda Civic car.

- Many people do not know that lubricants expire, and some watchmakers do not replace their oils until the bottles run out. Expired lubricants lose their effectiveness and may shorten a service cycle. Minimize any amount of chances that may cause a functional issue. Replacing expired oils is cheap in the grand scheme of things. Look out for the expiration date when you buy oils.

- Simple oilers: These are common oilers that you can find in any watch supply house. Although simple, it gets the job done. It is all you need to start if you are beginning to oil. If you have never oiled before, get these oilers. It is inexpensive and easy to see the amount of oil on the tip. It is also cost-efficient to replace if the tip gets broken. Watchmakers will have their preferences of what type of oilers to use. You just need a simple oiler to get the job done. In skilled hands, simple oilers can get the job done for anything.

Automatic Oilers: Automatic oilers are great if you repeatedly work on the same movement. It can dispense a specific amount of oil each time we use it. These will commonly be seen in manufacturers where the watchmakers are repeatedly working on the same set of calibres. If you are working at the retail level or in a shop where all types of movements come through your hands, set the quantity to the movement that comes through most frequently. Some watchmakers buy multiple versions of these for different types of jewels. Automatic oilers are used to save time and speed of work efficiency.

How to Regulate A Mechanical Watch

A mechanical watch movement has a power source. It forces a train of gears to turn. At the end of the train of gears is a locking device. This locking device allows and disallows the wheels to turn by locking and unlocking them. It is called escapement. It is made up of several parts:

- The escape wheel, which is the final gear

- The pallet fork which acts as locking and unlocking the gears

- The oscillator controls the rate at which the pallets lock and unlock the gears.

The escapement has the means to regulate the locking and unlocking of the gears for the gears to turn at the required speed. There are several types of the escapement, but the most modern timepieces will have a lever escapement. The Swiss lever is the most common. To regulate the watch, you need to control the oscillator's rate for it to unlock and lock the gears faster or slower, depending on the need. The oscillator in the watch is made up of several components in itself. However, we would focus on just two:

- The wheel, also known as the balance wheel

- The spring is also called the hairspring or balance spring.

Two things are very important to governing the rate of a watch: the balance wheel's dynamics and the spring's length.

- Changing the dynamics of the wheel, even by a small amount, will drastically change the watch's rate. However, this will only be done during the manufacturing stage and perhaps under other special circumstances. For example, when fine-tuning the rate of a watch, you would usually need to adjust the length of the balance spring effectively. In most cases, this is a very easy job as the design of the watch escapement provides a simple way to adjust the spring's length effectively.

- The regulator allows you to adjust the location of the curb pins along the length of the spring terminal curve. It will have the effect of lengthening and shortening the spring. If the spring is longer, then the rate will be slower. If the spring is shorter, then the rate of the watch will be faster. Some watch movements do not have a regulator.

- An example is the Rolex movements. It will require the adjustment of timing screws fitted to the balance wheel to adjust the rate. The Omega co-axial movement also requires this movement, while other movements may have weights that need to be adjusted on the balance wheel. In these cases, it is not recommended that you attempt to adjust the rate unless you are extremely confident, as the potential for damage is greater.

- Misaligning timing screws or balance weights can cause further problems and may be causing different rates depending on the watch's position. It is known as positional error.

In other to adjust a watch's daily rate:

- Locate the balance assembly and determine if a regulator is fitted. At most, mechanical watch movements will have one.

- By adjusting the regulator's position, you will move the curb pins along the length of the hairspring terminal curve to lengthen or shorten the spring effectively.

• The closer the curb pins are to the stud, the slower the watch will turn. The farther the curb pins are from the stud, the faster the watch will run.

How to Replace A Watch's Battery

When your watch battery dies, the watch will either stop working or will no longer give the right time. So, for example, you would need the following:

1. The new battery. Look out for the type of battery your watch uses and buy it. You can buy a single battery or a pack of batteries. Likewise, you can buy a pack of specific or various batteries.

2. A set of mini screwdrivers or just a little flat-head screwdriver.

3. A plier

4. A towel or a rag

5. Your watch.

For the cap watches,

Flip it over, and if you notice on the back of your watch, there is a cap. On that cap, if you look carefully around it, you will notice that in one spot, it has a little space compared to every other spot where it is tightly closed. So you would take your flat-head screwdriver and pry it open. Place the mini screwdrivers where you see a little space. Create leverage and push it open. If you have one of the twist watches, you will know if you have one of these watches.

You will need the pliers if you see little notches around the cap. Go ahead and place each side of the pliers in one of the notches. You are going to create pressure and twist it open. Remember Lefty - loosey, righty-tightly. It can be that you might need to use a little bit of strength the first time. Once you get it loose, you can use your hands to place it properly.

The screw type is very simple.

Take your Phillips screwdriver or flat-head screwdriver. Remove each screw. Having the screws in one spot and close to you would prevent losing them later. The last thing you want is a watch with a new battery and no cap.

Now, you can use their mini flat-head screwdriver to remove the cap. Now that you have removed all the watches' caps, you can verify the type of battery it uses. Using your mini flat-head screwdriver, remove the battery. Remember to always do this gently and place a new battery. Do that by inserting one side first and then pushing down. Next, place the cap back. Do this by using both hands and pressing the cap back in.

Conclusion

There are several things you should and should not do to your watch. First, take care of your watch. Do not store your watches anywhere that is damp or moist. If you know you are going to be doing something that is potentially going to damage the watch, the best thing is to take it off or have a beta watch specifically for that role.

Remember not to put too much force while whining, as this will break the crown. Always refer to your watch instruction manual for safe date-changing procedures. Finally, take your watches to a professional to keep your watch serviced and prevent further damage. Have a great experience with your watches!

Made in the USA
Thornton, CO
05/30/23 10:34:55

59baaa1d-9252-4736-95a1-8851eb3f1c4bR01